Polymers
All Around You!

2nd Edition

Contributing Author

Linda Woodward

Editor

Mickey Sarquis, Director
Center for Chemistry Education

Terrific Science Press
Miami University Middletown
Middletown, Ohio

Terrific Science Press
Miami University Middletown
4200 East University Boulevard
Middletown, OH 45042
513/727-3269
cce@muohio.edu
www.terrificscience.org

10   9   8   7   6   5   4   3

This monograph is intended for use by teachers, chemists, and properly supervised students. Users must follow procedures for the safe handling, use, and disposal of chemicals in accordance with local, state, federal, and institutional requirements. The cautions, warnings, and safety reminders associated with the doing of experiments and activities involving the use of chemicals and equipment contained in this publication have been compiled from sources believed to be reliable and to represent the best opinions on the subject as of the date of publication. Federal, state, local, or institutional standards, codes, and regulations should be followed and supercede information found in this monograph or its references. The user should check existing regulations as they are updated. No warranty, guarantee, or representation is made by the author or by Terrific Science Press as to the correctness or sufficiency of any information herein. Neither the author nor the publisher assumes any responsibility or liability for the use of the information herein, nor can it be assumed that all necessary warnings and precautionary measures are contained in this publication. Other or additional information or measures may be required or desirable because of particular or exceptional conditions or circumstances, or because of new or changed legislation.

ISBN: 1-883822-26-2

The publisher takes no responsibility for the use of any materials or methods described in this book, nor for the products thereof. Permission is granted to copy the materials for classroom use.

This material is based upon work supported in part by the National Science Foundation under Grant Number TPE-9153930, the U.S. Department of Education under Grant Number R168A10068, and the ACS Precollege Directorate of POLYED. Any opinions, findings, and conclusions or recommendations expressed in this material are those of the authors and do not necessarily reflect the views of the funding agencies.

Table of Contents

The author and editor wish to thank the following individuals who contributed to the development of *Polymers All Around You!*:

Lesson Contributors

Marie Sherman, Ursuline Academy, St. Louis, MO
Robert Becker, Kirkwood High School, Kirkwood, MO

Terrific Science Press Design and Production Team

Document Production Head: Amy Stander
Lead Writer and Editor: Susan Gertz
Technical Editing: Dot Lyon, Kate McCann
Technical Writing: Tom Schaffner
Production: Dawnetta Chapman, Dot Lyon, Kate McCann, Tom Schaffner
Cover Design and Layout: Susan Gertz
Illustrations: Susan Gertz and Carole Katz
Technical Review: Lynn Hogue

Photo Credits

Bicycle photo from Zipp/Compositech, currently Zipp Speed Weaponry, Speedway, IN
Prosthetic leg and foot photos from Sabolich Prosthetic & Research Center, Oklahoma City, OK
Downy® bottle photo from The Procter & Gamble Company, Cincinnati, OH
Soil Moist™ photo from JRM Chemical, Inc., Cleveland, OH
MiraCool photo from Stage 1 Online, Inc., Oviedo, FL
Fire-fighting gel photo from Barricade International, Inc., Hobe Sound, FL; *http://www.barricadegel.com.*
Car panels photo from Saturn Corporation, Spring Hill, TN

Introduction to Polymers

This booklet presents information and lessons on an exciting group of materials called *polymers.* To a chemist, polymers are special and interesting because they are the giants of the molecular world and because they have a tremendous variety of useful properties. The word *polymer* might be unfamiliar to you, but polymers themselves are probably the most familiar materials in your life. In fact, without polymers, life as we know it would not even exist.

Natural and Synthetic Polymers

Nearly all the materials that make up living organisms involve polymers. These include such basic building blocks of life as collagen (the main protein component of connective tissue such as bone, cartilage, and tendons); keratin (the main component of protective coverings such as hair, hoofs, claws, feathers, beaks, and nails); enzymes; certain hormones; hemoglobin; DNA; starch; and cellulose. Many of the natural materials we use every day are also polymers. These include cotton, wool, wood, and latex.

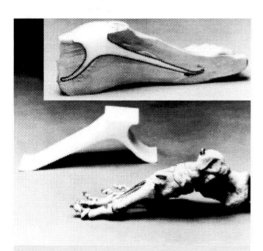

Plastic Arch Mimics Life

Most of us take the biomechanics of walking for granted. But walking is no simple matter for those who have lost a foot or leg. The Sabolich Prosthetic and Research Center has developed a plastic prosthetic foot that mimics the human arch. It simulates the function of the bones and tendons of the human foot. The prosthetic foot builds up, stores, transfers, and releases energy as a person walks or runs, allowing a more natural gait. A cosmetic covering, including vein lines and toenails can be added.

Our technological age is primarily an age of synthetic polymers; few, if any, products of technology are more pervasive in our lives than these. Polymers bring us an amazingly wide range of products—from the control panels of vehicles that explore outer space to artificial joints used to repair human bodies. We can scarcely imagine living without polymer-based synthetic fabrics, construction materials, food packaging, and vehicles. (For a table of everyday polymer products, see page 7.) Synthetic polymers are useful and economical. While petroleum is used to make polymer products, this usage accounts for less than 2% of all crude oil pumped each year. (Most crude oil is used for energy production.) Recovery and recycling of preconsumer polymer materials save resources and have been common practices for many years. As manufacturing technology advances, we are also recovering more postconsumer waste and incorporating it into more new products. Some of the newest polymer products use as much as 100% recycled postconsumer waste.

Properties of Polymers

One of the reasons polymers are so useful is their variety. Scientists and engineers have been able to develop polymers with many different properties. Polymers may be flexible or rigid, transparent or opaque, heat-resistant or heat-conductive, waterproof or water-soluble, electrically insulating or electrically conductive, hard or soft, and elastic or inelastic.

What accounts for this variety? The word *polymer* provides some clues: *poly* means many and *mer* means unit. A polymer is a huge, chainlike molecule made by combining many small molecules called *monomers*. *Mono* means one; a monomer is one unit. A wide variety of polymers with different properties can be created by bonding different monomers together.

An example of a common polymer is *polyethylene*. It is made by bonding together many monomers called ethylene (CH_2=CH_2), as shown below. Polyethylene molecules are actually made of thousands of ethylene units linked together—many more than we have room to show here. Polyethylene can exist in either a high-density form (abbreviated as HDPE) or a low-density form (abbreviated as LDPE). (The Recycling Codes table on page 9 shows some typical uses for each polymer type.)

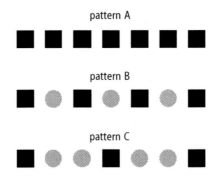

ethylene
monomer

polyethylene
polymer

Teflon® is another common polymer (the nonreactive polymer typically used as a heat-resistant coating). A molecule of Teflon looks much like polyethylene, except that each hydrogen atom (H) is replaced by a fluorine atom (F). The monomer that is used to make Teflon is tetrafluoroethylene (CF_2=CF_2). How about polyvinyl chloride (PVC)? The monomer used is chloroethylene (CH_2=$CHCl$), and the resulting polymer has a chlorine atom (Cl) on every other carbon.

Polyethylene, Teflon, and PVC are each made from a single type of monomer, as shown in pattern A below. Some polymers, such as polyethylene terephthalate (PET or PETE), polyester, and nylon, are made from the combination of two or more different monomers. Two common combinations are shown in patterns B and C.

pattern A

■ ■ ■ ■ ■ ■ ■

pattern B

■ ● ■ ● ■ ● ■

pattern C

■ ● ● ■ ● ● ■

Everyday Polymer Products

• answering machine • Astroturf® • audiotape • awning • baby bottle • balloon • Band-Aid® • beverage box • bicycle • boat • bobber • book bag • briefcase • bubble gum • bubble wrap • butane lighter • button • camera • car battery • carpet • caulking • CD-ROM disk • cellophane tape • Chap Stick® tube • checkers • coaster • coffee stirrer • comb • compact • computer • computer disk • computer mouse • contacts • Corvette® • credit card • dishpan • disposable diaper • disposable razor • egg carton • electrical tape • epoxy glue • eraser • exercise mat • extension cord • eyeglasses • false eyelashes • false teeth • fan belt • fast-food container • FAX machine • fishing line • flea collar • floor tile • floor wax • fluorescent light cover • flute • foam rubber pillow • food storage container • food wrap • football helmet • Friendly Plastic® • Frisbee® • furniture polish • galoshes • Grow Creatures® • guitar string • hair dryer • hang glider • hearing aid • hockey puck • house paint • ice chest • ice cube tray • index tabs • insulated foam cup • insulation • jewelry • keyboard • knapsack • lawn chair • life raft • lipstick tube • luggage • lunch tray • mannequin • margarine tub • measuring tape • microfilm • microwave cookware • milk jug • miniblinds • model car • model plane • mop • motor oil bottle • motorcycle helmet • movie film • nylon clothing • overhead projector • pacifier • paintbrush • panty hose • parachute • pen • pencil case • photographic film • Ping-Pong ball • plastic cup • plastic flowerpot • plastic flowers • plastic shoe box • plastic wrap • plastic utensils • playing cards • plumber's putty • polyester clothing • pot handle • protractor • radio • raincoat • reflector • refrigerator • rubber band • rubber duckie • rubber gloves • ruler • safety glass • safety glasses • sail • sandals • school desk • seat cushion • shampoo bottles • shoe polish • shoe soles • shoestring tips • shower curtain • shower door • shuttle cock • Silly Putty® • skateboard wheels • slides • Slime® • sneakers • snorkel • soft-drink bottle • sponge • store sign • straw • Styrofoam® • sun visor • sunglasses • superglue • surfboard • swim fins • synthetic fabrics • tape dispenser • Teflon cookware • telephone • tennis racket • Thermos® bottle • thread spool • thread • tire • toilet seat • toothbrush • toothpaste tube • transparency • trash bag • trash can • Tygon® tubing • umbrella • Velcro® • vinyl siding • vinyl wall covering • vitamin capsule • volleyball • wallet • water pipe • Weed Whacker® • welcome mat • wet suit • whistle • white glue • wig • windbreaker • windshield • windshield wiper • yarn • zipper • zipper-type plastic bag

Reference: National Science Teachers Association. *Polymer Chemistry, A Teaching Package for Pre-College Teachers;* Washington, DC, 1986.

Polymer Recycling

As our population grows, the amount of garbage we produce also grows. At the same time, more stringent environmental regulations mean that landfills and incinerators are more difficult to site, take longer to build, and cost more money. In addition, at the current rate of use, landfills have an average lifespan of only about 10 years. Thus, any reduction in the volume of trash going into a landfill will increase the landfill's lifespan and potentially save money and resources.

Plastics (synthetic polymers) make up about 20% by volume of the municipal solid waste system, with plastic containers, packaging, and wraps accounting for about 8%. Paper and paperboard contribute 34%; food and yard wastes, about 17%; metals, 12%; and glass, 2%. Most of these materials are recyclable, and many communities have initiated programs to remove them from the waste stream.

To be successful, recycling programs must offer some advantage to manufacturers. Aluminum recycling, for example, has been highly successful because tremendous energy savings make it economically desirable. Although the advantage of recycling some materials (such as aluminum) is primarily energy savings, the advantage of recycling polymers is the savings of nonrenewable petroleum resources. During the 1990s, the polymer industry developed an array of technologies for recycling and reusing polymers. For example, in 1991, manufacturers announced that soft-drink bottles made of polyethylene terephthalate (PETE) could be recycled, not only into picnic benches and other nonfood items, but also into new soft-drink bottles. This advance was made possible by a new technique for breaking the polymer down into its monomers, then rebuilding the polymer. Today it's common to see postconsumer recycled polymers used to make fencing, playground equipment, and clothing.

A variety of methods is used to make the sorting of plastics for recycling more feasible. The plastics industry has adopted a coding system to help recyclers identify the six types of plastics typically used in making bottles and other containers. These codes (shown in the table on page 9) consist of a triangle formed by three arrows, with a number in the center and distinguishing letters under the triangle. The codes are molded or imprinted on the bottom of most plastic containers. In addition, other more sophisticated technologies to sort plastics are in use. One such system uses photoelectric sensors to separate PETE, high-density polyethylene (HDPE), and vinyl (V) bottles.

A Good Night's Sleep

The next time you fall asleep, you may be sleeping on what was once a soft-drink bottle. Some bed pillows are filled with soft fibers made from PETE plastic recycled from soft-drink bottles and other sources. Recycled PETE can be used for many kinds of products. In the year 2000, the average household generated 34 pounds of PETE bottles. That's enough plastic to make
- three square feet of carpet,
- three sweaters,
- fiberfill for three ski jackets, and
- fiberfill for three sleeping bags.

National Association for PET Container Resources "Fun Facts About PET." http://www.napcor.com/funfacts.html

Recycling Codes

Recycling Symbol	Name of Polymer	Sample Uses
1 PETE	polyethylene terephthalate	• soft-drink bottles • carpets • fiberfill • rope • scouring pads • fabrics • Mylar® tape (cassette and computer)
2 HDPE	high-density polyethylene	• milk jugs • detergent bottles • bags • plastic lumber • garden furniture • flowerpots • trash cans
3 V	vinyl	• cooking oil bottles • drainage and sewer pipes • tile • bird feeders • institutional furniture • credit cards
4 LDPE	low-density polyethylene	• bags • Elmer's® glue bottles and other squeeze bottles • wrapping films • container lids
5 PP	polypropylene	• yogurt containers • automobile batteries • bottles • lab equipment • carpets • rope • wrapping films
6 PS	polystyrene	• disposable cups and utensils • toys • lighting and signs • construction • foam containers and insulation
7 other	all other polymers	• catsup, snack, and other food containers • lotion, toothpaste, and cosmetic containers

Safety First

The hands-on science investigations in this book will add fun and excitement to science education in your classroom. However, even the simplest activity can become dangerous when the proper safety precautions are ignored, when the activity is done incorrectly, or when the activity is performed by students without proper supervision. The science investigations in this book have been extensively reviewed by classroom teachers of elementary grades and by university scientists. We have done all we can to assure the safety of the activities as written. It's up to you to ensure their safe execution!

- Always practice activities yourself before performing them with your class. This is the only way to become thoroughly familiar with the procedures and materials required for an activity, and familiarity will help prevent potentially hazardous (or merely embarrassing) mishaps. In addition, you may find variations that will make the activity more meaningful to your students.

- Read each activity carefully and observe all safety precautions and disposal procedures. Collect and read the Materials Safety Data Sheets (MSDSs) for all of the chemicals used in your experiments. MSDSs provide physical property data, toxicity information, and handling and disposal specifications for chemicals. They can be obtained upon request from manufacturers and distributors of these chemicals or from World Wide Web sites such as *http://hazard.com/msds/*. In fact, MSDSs are often shipped with the chemicals when they are ordered. These should be collected and made available to students, faculty, or parents for information about specific chemicals used in these activities.

- Special safety instructions are not given for everyday classroom materials being used in a typical manner. Use common sense when working with hot, sharp, or breakable objects, such as flames, scissors, or glassware. Keep tables or desks covered to avoid stains. Clean up spills to prevent falls.

- In some activities, potentially hazardous items such as ovens are to be used only by the teacher.

- When introducing an activity that involves smelling potentially unknown odors, instruct the students about protecting themselves. Tell them never to smell an unknown substance by placing it directly under the nose. Show the students how to use the wafting procedure (at right) and remind them to avoid prolonged inhalation of objectionable odors—such odors are typically not good for us. If an odor cannot be detected through wafting, the material can be waved closer to the nose.

To smell unknown odors, hold the container approximately 6 inches from the nose and, using the free hand, gently waft the air above the open container toward the nose.

Testing Polymer Densities

For plastics to be recycled, they must be separated by type. One method for separating plastics depends on the fact that different plastics have different densities. The plastics to be recycled are shredded, then placed into a liquid such as water. The plastics that are more dense than water will sink, but those less dense than water will float. The floaters and sinkers are recovered separately, and the process is repeated with other liquids having different densities. In this lesson, you will identify six different categories of plastics based on their relative densities.

Materials

✓ samples of plastic types 1–6 (see Recycling Codes table on page 9) ✓ Styrofoam egg cartons or many small containers ✓ craft sticks or other stirrers ✓ water ✓ vegetable oil ✓ glycerin ✓ 70% isopropyl rubbing alcohol

Advance Preparation

❶ Cut the plastic samples into small pieces that can be differentiated by color, size, and/or shape. (Keep a key to which samples represent each type of plastic.)
❷ Make up an alcohol/water solution that is three parts isopropyl rubbing alcohol and two parts water. ❸ Prepare a set of four liquids (alcohol/water solution, water, vegetable oil, and glycerin) for each group of students by pouring the various liquids into separate egg carton wells or into other containers.

Procedure

❶ Drop a piece of plastic into one of the liquids. If it does not sink immediately, push it gently down below the surface with a craft stick and observe until it stops moving. Record whether it sinks or floats in that particular liquid. ❷ Repeat step 1 with the same type of plastic in the other liquids and record your results. ❸ Repeat steps 1 and 2 with samples of the other plastics. ❹ Use the table at left to determine the identity of your samples. ❺ Notice that polyethylene terephthalate (PETE) and vinyl (V) give the same results. You can tell them apart by bending a sample. A piece of vinyl will whiten when bent, but PETE will not.

Type of plastic \ Floats on	Vegetable Oil	Alcohol/Water	Water	Glycerin
PETE	no	no	no	no
HDPE	no	no	yes	yes
V	no	no	no	no
LDPE	no	yes	yes	yes
PP	yes	yes	yes	yes
PS	no	no	no	yes

References

The Shaping of Things to Come; The Society of Plastics Industry, Inc., c/o The Naidus Group, Inc., P.O. Box 12057, Hauppauge, NY 11788-9705.

Kolb, K.E.; Kolb, D.K. "Identifying Plastics by Density (LTE)," *Journal of Chemical Education.* 1993, 70, 174.

Gluep

This lesson turns common white glue into gooey fun. By combining white glue, borax (sodium borate), and water in various proportions, you will experiment to determine the best formulation for making a fun polymer called Gluep. Like Silly Putty and Slime, Gluep has some properties of a liquid (for example, it flows) and some properties of a solid (for example, it breaks).

What makes Gluep so different from the glue, borax, and water that are used to make it? Crosslinking. But more on this later. First, let's consider what's in the glue that makes all this possible. Most brands of white glue contain millions of long chains of a polymer called *polyvinyl acetate* (PVAc) that have been dissolved in water. In glue, these PVAc chains slip and slide over one another like strands of freshly cooked wet spaghetti. Although they can slip and slide, the polyvinyl acetate chains are so long that they interfere with each other, causing the glue to be rather thick and to pour more slowly than water.

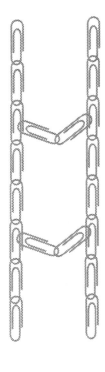

When you add borax to glue, you cause the polyvinyl acetate polymer chains to be linked together—just as rungs link the two sides of a ladder. The borax forms bridges between the polymer chains, binding (cross-linking) them together and producing a gel-like material that is more viscous than the glue. The phenomena of crosslinking can be shown via the kinesthetic activity done in Part C of this lesson or by showing how the properties of two long chains of paper clips change when they are joined by a few "cross-linking" clips as shown at left.

As you will learn, Gluep has a variety of interesting properties. These properties vary with the amount of cross-linking, which depends on the proportions of polyvinyl acetate, borax, and water that are used. Which combination of ingredients is right? The perfect product is the one whose properties best match the intended use. So you decide!

Safety for Parts A and B

Do not give Gluep to students younger than 5 years of age. They may try to taste it, and it could get stuck in the student's throat. Some people have an allergic reaction to dry borax. Students should not handle the dry borax, which is moderately toxic. You should use adequate ventilation when preparing the solution, and wash your hands if contact with the dry borax occurs. Instruct students to wash their hands after contact with the Gluep.

Disposal for Parts A and B

Store Gluep in a sealed plastic bag because it will dry out. To retard mold growth, keep it in the refrigerator. When you are through with your Gluep, discard it in the trash, *not* down the drain. Do not place Gluep on natural wood furniture as it will leave a water mark. It may stick to other materials. If Gluep sticks to a carpet, pour on some vinegar to break down the gel, then wash the area with soap and water.

Part A: Make Some Gluep
Which Gluep recipe makes the best product?

Materials

✓small (3 ounce) paper cups ✓craft sticks ✓borax, available from grocery stores ✓Elmer's white glue, Elmer's school glue, or any brand of white glue (all glues do not work equally well; test them in advance) ✓water ✓measuring spoons or other measuring devices such as graduated, disposable medicine cups ✓food color ✓3-inch x 5-inch colored recipe cards (use green, blue, pink, and yellow to match the four colors in a box of food color)

Advance Preparation

❶ Make the saturated borax solution by stirring ¼ cup borax into 1 quart warm water. Allow any undissolved solid to settle to the bottom before using. ❷ Prepare color-coded recipe cards with the following recipes:

green: 15 mL (1 tablespoon) glue, 15 mL (1 tablespoon) water, 10 mL (2 teaspoons) borax solution

blue: 15 mL (1 tablespoon) glue, 30 mL (2 tablespoons) water, 10 mL (2 teaspoons) borax solution

pink: 15 mL (1 tablespoon) glue, no water, 10 mL (2 teaspoons) borax solution

yellow: 15 mL (1 tablespoon) glue, 15 mL (1 tablespoon) water, 20 mL (4 teaspoons) borax solution

Procedure

❶ Select a recipe card and use the ingredient amounts in the following procedure. ❷ Measure out the white glue and pour it into a small paper cup. ❸ Observe the glue. What does the glue feel like?...smell like?...look like? ❹ Measure out the water and add it to the glue in the cup. Stir with a craft stick. Repeat the above observations. What does the mixture feel like?...smell like?...look like? ❺ To the glue mixture, add a drop or two of the food color that corresponds to the color of your recipe card and stir. ❻ Measure out the borax solution. Get someone to help you so that one person stirs with the craft stick as the other adds the borax (cross-linker) to the glue solution. ❼ Once the Gluep is formed, remove it from the cup and knead it for several minutes. Repeat your observations. What does the Gluep feel like?...smell like?...look like? ❽ Compare your product with those made using other recipes. If you like another product better than yours, make some of it!

Part B: Observe the Properties of Gluep

If solids have a rigid shape of their own and liquids flow to take up the shape of their container, what is Gluep?

Materials

✓Gluep ✓coin or small object ✓cup ✓plastic bag ✓washable marker or fluorescent highlighter

Procedure

❶ Roll the Gluep into a ball and place it in the palm of your hand. Does the ball keep its shape? ❷ Pat the Gluep between your hands and try to form a thin film. Hold the film at one end and observe. ❸ Drop a ball of Gluep onto a clean, nonwood tabletop. Does it bounce? How quickly does it begin to spread out? ❹ Use coins or small objects to make imprints in the Gluep. Do these imprints last? ❺ Roll the Gluep into a tube shape and slowly pull it apart while holding it at both ends. ❻ Re-form the tube and pull it apart quickly. ❼ Write your name or draw a face on a plastic bag with a washable marker or fluorescent highlighter. Shape the Gluep into a small pancake, place it over the design, and remove it carefully. What do you see? Try kneading the colored Gluep. How could you get even more color into your Gluep?

Part C: Demonstrate Cross-Linking

Procedure

❶ Ask for eight volunteers to demonstrate cross-linking. (You may want to warn them that they will be holding hands.) Tell the class that each volunteer represents a *monomer* (one unit). ❷ Have monomers move freely around the room. ❸ Have two groups of four monomers join hands to form two short segments of a polymer chain. *Poly* means many and *mer* means unit, so a polymer is many units linked together. ❹ Have each polymer move around the room with hands still linked. Point out that they can move relatively freely just like the polymer (polyvinyl acetate) molecules in white glue. ❺ Explain that the borax solution contains units that act as *cross-linkers* to connect the polymer chains together. Play the role of the cross-linker by holding the arm of one monomer in the middle of each of the polymer chains. (See figure.) ❻ Have the polymers try to move around as before. Some movement is still possible, but it will be much more restricted than before the cross-linker was added.

References

"Glue Polymer," *Chain Gang—The Chemistry of Polymers;* Sarquis, A.M., Ed.; Science in Our World Series; Terrific Science: Middletown, OH, 1999.

Polyvinyl Alcohol

In this lesson, you study films and fibers made of another polymer—
polyvinyl alcohol—and use this polymer to make a gooey cross-linked product:
slime! Polyvinyl alcohol (PVA) is used in many products you use every day,
including hair gels, cosmetics, printing inks, and textile finishes.

Water-soluble polymers like PVA are ideal for making items that are supposed to
dissolve. For example, hospitals pack laundry in PVA bags. Laundry workers can
place the bags directly into washing machines without opening them. This limits
the spread of infectious microbes. PVA bags are also used to hold premeasured
amounts of powders, such as pesticides, that are mixed with water before use.

Chemists are able to make PVA with different degrees of water-solubility. This is
done by varying the reaction conditions, which changes the number of alcohol
groups on the molecule. PVA with a large number of alcohol groups is more water-
soluble than PVA with a lesser number of alcohol groups. The more water-soluble
form of PVA dissolves in either hot or cold water. The less water-soluble form
requires higher temperatures for dissolving to occur.

Advance Preparation for All Parts

Purchase polyvinyl alcohol (PVA) solution (4%), powder, or film: All parts of
this lesson require a 4% PVA solution that can be purchased pre-made or made
from PVA powder or film.

The 4% PVA solution and PVA powder are available from Flinn Scientific, Batavia,
IL; 800/452-1261; *http://www.flinnsci.com.* If you use powder, be sure to get
99–100% hydrolyzed PVA power with a molar mass of at least 100,000.

PVA film is available in the form of water-soluble laundry bags. The method for
making a 4% solution with PVA film (described later in this section) is based on
using a 26-inch x 33-inch PVA bag that is 1 Mil thick. Bags with these dimensions
are sold in cases of 100 by the Associated Bag Company, Milwaukee, WI;
800/926-6100; *http://www.associatedbag.com.* A less expensive but not always
available source is American Science & Surplus, Skokie, IL; 847/647-0011;
http://www.sciplus.com. You may also be able to get PVA bags from your local
hospital. If the bag you use has different dimensions or thickness than the bag
specified, adjust as needed to approximate a 4% solution. (Note: The PVA bag
specifically called for in Part A of the lesson can be any size or thickness.)

To prepare 4% PVA solution from PVA powder: ❶ Gradually sprinkle
40 g (⅓ cup) PVA powder into 1 L water in a microwave-safe container, stirring
constantly. (Do not make more than 1 liter at a time.) ❷ Stir the solution and
place it in a full-size microwave oven. Heat the solution on high for 8 minutes,
stirring every 1–2 minutes. (Heating time may vary, depending on the power of
your microwave.) ❸ Allow the solution to cool before using. If a slimy or gooey
layer appears on the top, skim it off and discard it in the trash. Store the cooled
solution in a labeled, closed container, such as a 2-L soft-drink bottle.

To prepare 4% PVA solution from PVA film: ❶ Cut the PVA bag into small pieces and place them into 875 mL hot water (60°C or 140°F). Stir to dissolve. ❷ Allow the solution to cool before using. Store the cooled solution in a labeled, closed container, such as a 2-L soft-drink bottle.

Part A: Make and Test PVA Film

Materials

✓ polyvinyl alcohol (PVA) bag ✓ paper or plastic cups ✓ craft stick or other stirrer ✓ hot and cold water ✓ 4% PVA solution ✓ 3 pie pans

Procedure

❶ Observe the polyvinyl alcohol (PVA) bag. ❷ Place a small piece of the bag in a cup of cold water and stir. What happens? Place a small piece of the bag in a cup of hot water and stir. What happens? ❸ Allow the hot mixture to cool. Test both mixtures you have made by rubbing small amounts of each between your fingers. (Try one, then the other.) What do you observe? ❹ Pour the rest of each mixture into its own pie pan and label each. ❺ Rub a small amount of the 4% PVA solution (made in Advance Preparation) through your fingers. How does it compare to the mixtures from step 3? ❻ Pour 4% PVA solution into a third pie pan to just cover the bottom. ❼ Allow the water to evaporate from all pans. Peel the PVA film from each pan and cut each into several narrow strips, keeping the strips from each pan separate. ❽ Dip a strip from each sample in cool water and another in hot water. What happens? How do strips from the three film samples compare? ❾ Wash your hands.

Part B: Make PVA Fibers and Investigate Their Flexibility

Materials

✓ 4% polyvinyl alcohol (PVA) solution ✓ small glass container ✓ (optional) food color ✓ acetone (available at hardware stores; nail polish remover contains too much water to be used) ✓ tweezers or forceps ✓ large plastic bag

Safety

Acetone is flammable. Read the precautions on the labels and do the lesson in a well-ventilated area.

Procedure

❶ Pour 4% polyvinyl alcohol (PVA) solution into the small glass container to a depth of about 2 cm. Add a drop of food color if desired and mix well. ❷ Tip the container slightly and slowly pour in a 2-cm layer of acetone. The acetone will float on the PVA solution, and a white layer of PVA will form at the interface of the two layers. (See figure.) ❸ Use tweezers or forceps to pick up the interface layer and slowly pull it straight up and out of the container. (See figure.) Usually a strand 40–60 cm long can be pulled out. ❹ Lay the strand on the plastic bag to dry. Remove additional strands until the PVA layer is completely used up. ❺ Dry the strands overnight. The next day they will be flexible but inelastic. Dip a strand briefly in cool water so it becomes elastic again. Try dipping a strand in hot water. What happens?

PVA fiber

acetone

PVA layer out of solution

PVA solution

Part C: Make Your Own Slime

Materials

✓small (3 ounce) paper or plastic cups ✓craft stick ✓4% polyvinyl alcohol (PVA) solution ✓saturated borax solution (prepared as in Gluep lesson) ✓(optional) food color

Safety

Do not give slime to students younger than 5 years of age. They may try to taste it, and it could get stuck in the student's throat. Some people have an allergic reaction to dry borax. Students should not handle the dry borax, which is moderately toxic. Use adequate ventilation when preparing the solution, and wash your hands if contact with the dry borax occurs. Instruct students to wash their hands after contact with the slime.

Procedure

Follow the directions for Part A of the Gluep lesson (see page 13), but use this recipe: 30 mL (2 tablespoons) 4% polyvinyl alcohol (PVA) solution, 2.5 mL (½ teaspoon) saturated borax solution, and no extra water.

References

Sherman, M.C. "Producing Fibers of Poly(Vinyl Alcohol): An Alternative Method," *Journal of Chemical Education.* 1992, 69, 883.

Sarquis, A.M.; Kibbey, B.; Smyth, E. "Make-It-Yourself Slime," *Science Activities for Elementary Classrooms;* Flinn Scientific: Batavia, IL, 1989.

Sarquis, J.L.; Hogue, L.; Sarquis, A.M.; Woodward, L. "Non-Newtonian Fluids—Liquids or Solids?" *Investigating Solids, Liquids, and Gases with TOYS;* McGraw-Hill: New York, 1997.

Defoaming Packing Peanuts

Puffy packing peanuts are ideal for cushioning delicate items. When evenly distributed in a rigid container, they can easily absorb impacts and are lightweight to boot. So why do packing peanuts have such great properties? It's because they are foamed; that is, they are full of gas pockets. Some packing peanuts are made of foamed *polystyrene* (a synthetic polymer commonly called Styrofoam), and others are made of foamed cornstarch, a natural polymer.

You can defoam both types of packing peanuts by mechanically smashing them. But you can also defoam them chemically with two common solvents: water for the cornstarch peanuts and acetone for the Styrofoam ones. Both solvents work on their respective types of packing peanuts by creeping between the solid polymer networks and causing the polymers to soften. In the process, the packing peanuts collapse as the trapped gas escapes. Surprisingly small amounts of solvent will defoam large amounts of foamed polymer.

Materials

✓Styrofoam packing peanuts ✓cornstarch packing peanuts (such as RENATURE® Special, available from Storopack, Inc., Cincinnati, OH; 800/827-7225; *http://www.storopackinc.com*) ✓acetone (available from hardware stores; nail polish remover contains too much water to use) ✓3 wide-mouth containers ✓water ✓plastic bag

Safety

Acetone is flammable. Read the precautions on the labels and do the lesson in a well-ventilated area.

Procedure

❶ Pour acetone in a wide-mouth container to a depth of 1–2 cm. ❷ Add a few Styrofoam peanuts, stir, and observe. ❸ Continue adding small batches of Styrofoam peanuts, keeping count of the peanuts added. Allow each batch to collapse before adding more, and make sure that all of the peanuts touch the acetone. Repeat until no more peanuts will collapse or you run out of peanuts. ❹ Repeat steps 1–3 using warm water and cornstarch peanuts. ❺ Pour any excess acetone off the solid in the Styrofoam mixture into a wide-mouth container. Place the container in a well-ventilated area and allow the acetone to evaporate. Pour off excess water from the cornstarch mixture and rinse it down the drain. ❻ Pour the collapsed Styrofoam and cornstarch peanuts onto separate plastic bags and allow them to dry. These solids will stick to other surfaces, so be sure to keep them on the plastic bags. ❼ When the collapsed peanuts are completely dry, observe. The solid polymers can be discarded in the trash.

Reference

"Taking the Foam Out of Styrofoam," *Chain Gang—The Chemistry of Polymers*; Sarquis, A.M., Ed.; Science in Our World Series; Terrific Science: Middletown, OH, 1999.

Polymer Stretch Test

Have you ever shot a rubberband? The shooting action happens because, even though the rubber band is stretchy, it returns to its original shape immediately after the external force is removed. Balloons and sewing elastic behave the same way. There are several other polymer products that are designed to stretch in a specific manner. In this lesson, you will investigate the stretch in plastic grocery bags and in a common plumbing product called Teflon tape. Both of these products are designed to stretch more in one direction than in the other.

Grocery bags are typically made of a thin *polyethylene* film and the Teflon tape from *polytetrafluoroethylene* film. During the manufacturing process for both items, molten polymer is stretched in one direction along a conveyor belt. This causes the long polymer chains to align side by side in the machine direction, as shown in the following figure. Each of these long polymer chains is held tightly together by strong chemical bonds (covalent bonds). These bonds don't let the grocery bag and Teflon tape films have much stretch in the machined direction, even though the films do stretch in the non-machined direction.

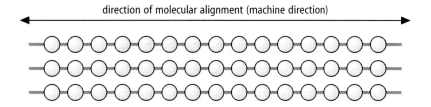

direction of molecular alignment (machine direction)

Teflon and polyethylene are made of polymer chains that are aligned parallel to each other lengthwise.

Part A: Grocery Bag Stretch
Can you find the machine direction of a plastic grocery bag?

Materials

✓ plastic grocery bag (with text printed on it) ✓ scissors ✓ ruler ✓ permanent marker

Procedure

❶ Define lengthwise as being from the handles of the bag toward the bottom; define widthwise as around the middle of the bag. Cut a 15-cm x 15-cm square from a grocery bag. Use a permanent marker to label the lengthwise and widthwise directions. Measure and record the actual length and width of the square. Let the marker dry before continuing. ❷ Test the stretchability of the square in both the lengthwise and widthwise directions by gently pulling the square in the appropriate direction. Don't pull so hard that the piece breaks. After each stretch, measure and record the dimensions of the plastic before stretching it in the other direction. Does the bag stretch evenly in both directions? Which direction do you think the bag was machined in? ❸ Cut out a strip of the bag that has printing on it. Can you distort the printing? What can you do to return the print to its regular size?

Part B: Other Stretchy Things

Materials

✓ 4- to 5-inch strip of 1-inch-wide Teflon tape (also called PTFE thread-seal tape, available from hardware or discount department stores in the plumbing section; also available from Fisher Scientific, Pittsburgh, PA; 800/766-7000; *http://www.fishersci.com*) ✓ 4- to 5-inch strip of sewing elastic ✓ ½- to ⅝-inch-wide rubber band (size 82, 84, or 107) ✓ balloon

Procedure

❶ Experiment with stretching the sewing elastic, rubber band, balloon, and Teflon tape in both lengthwise and widthwise directions. ❷ Based on how they stretched, divide the materials into two or more groups and explain your reasoning for their classification. Which group would the grocery bag fit into?

Part C: Cockeyed Messages

Use the stretch properties of Teflon tape to send a secret message to a friend.

Materials

✓ 4- to 5-inch strips of 1-inch-wide Teflon tape ✓ ballpoint pen

Procedure

❶ What do you think would happen to the shapes of the letters if you wrote a message on the Telfon tape and stretched it? Try it! ❷ Take a new strip of Teflon tape. Write a brief, secret message on this piece of tape and stretch the tape to hide the message from all but the intended reader. ❸ Give the message to a friend, and explain how to return the tape to its original shape to read the message.

References

Becker, R. "Teflon Tape," *Chem 13 News.* 1994, 234, 8.

"The Stretch Test," *Chain Gang—The Chemistry of Polymers;* Sarquis, A.M., Ed.; Science in Our World Series; Terrific Science: Middletown, OH, 1999.

Sarquis, A.M.; Woodward, L. "Grocery Bag Stretch," *Science Projects for Holidays Throughout the Year;* McGraw-Hill: New York, 1999.

Skewering Polymers

Can you pierce a water-filled plastic bag with sharp pencils without the bag leaking? Yes. It's not magic—it's the nature of the polymer molecules of the bag. The bag is made of a thin sheet of many long, intertwined polyethylene molecules that provide flexibility and stretchiness to the bag. When you poke a sharp pencil through the bag, the polymer stretches and contours around the pencil, forming a relatively tight seal.

Can you push a bamboo skewer through an inflated balloon without popping the balloon? Yes, if you push the skewer through the right areas of the balloon. The balloon is made of a thin latex sheet of many long, intertwined polymer molecules. When the balloon is inflated, these molecules become highly stretched in areas like the middle of the balloon. A skewer pushed through a stretched area will cause the balloon to tear and pop. However, if you push the skewer through a relatively thicker, unstretched region of the balloon, such as the tie end, the chains stretch around the skewer and allow it to pass through without the balloon popping.

Part A: Pencil It In

Materials

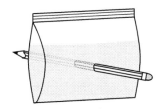

✓ zipper-type plastic bag ✓ water ✓ several sharp pencils

Procedure

❶ Fill the bag with water and zip it closed. ❷ Push the sharpened pencils through the sides of the bag. Practice this one over a sink until you learn the method.

Part B: Balloon on a Stick

Materials

✓ balloon ✓ bamboo skewer ✓ cooking oil

Procedure

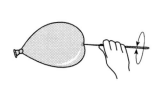

❶ Inflate a balloon to about half its maximum volume and tie it off. ❷ Dip the tip of the bamboo skewer into the cooking oil. ❸ Use a gentle, twisting motion to insert the skewer into the thick nipple end of the balloon, opposite the tie end. Don't jerk back as the point pierces the balloon. This could cause it to pop. ❹ Continue pushing the skewer through the balloon until it emerges from the tie end. Pull the skewer out slowly through the tie end. Place your hand over the holes to feel any air leaking out. ❺ To show that this is a real balloon, jab the skewer through the middle area to pop it!

Reference

Sarquis, A.M.; Sarquis, J.L. "Needle Through a Balloon," *Fun with Chemistry: A Guidebook of K–12 Activities,* Vol. 1; Institute for Chemical Education, University of Wisconsin: Madison, WI, 1991.

Shrinking Plastic

How a plastic behaves when heated is a physical property. *Polystyrene* (PS) and some other plastics can be softened and remolded any number of times when heated. They are called *thermoplastics.* Other plastics, called *thermoset plastics,* do not soften when reheated; they retain their original shape. Thermoset plastics are particularly useful in pot handles or other items that are regularly exposed to heat.

The shrinking nature of the PS used in this lesson results from the way it is manufactured; it is first heated, then stretched into a thin film and quickly cooled. This sudden cooling "freezes" the molecules of PS in a stretched-out position. When the PS is heated once again, the molecules relax and the PS returns to its original, unstretched size. The plastic shrinks in some (not all) directions, but the mass does not change.

Depending on how the PS is stretched during manufacturing, it may not shrink uniformly when heated. PS made specifically for shrinking craft projects is manufactured in such a way that it shrinks very uniformly and stays square even after shrinking. Other types of PS may not shrink evenly. Foamed PS (Styrofoam) shrinks when heated, but this is largely due to the loss of the gas that was originally trapped in the foam (as part of the degassing process).

Safety for All Parts

Use only #6 plastic. Do not heat other plastics, as some produce noxious odors.

Advance Preparation for All Parts

Preheat the oven to 325°F. Since oven temperatures can vary, test the oven you plan to use in advance to determine the best baking time.

Part A: Shrunken Polystyrene Crafts

Materials

✓ clear, clean polystyrene (PS) containers (#6 recycle code) such as deli containers ✓ several different-colored, fine- or medium-point permanent markers ✓ toaster oven or conventional oven (*not* a convection oven or microwave) ✓ aluminum foil ✓ oven mitt ✓ (optional) hole punch ✓ (optional) scissors

Procedure

❶ Draw a design on a small piece of polystyrene (PS) with permanent markers. If desired, cut out the design. ❷ Place the PS square on aluminum foil and put it in the 325°F oven. Heat until the plastic piece curls up then uncurls and flattens. (This typically takes about 1 minute.) ❸ Use an oven mitt to carefully remove the plastic and foil from the hot oven. Allow to cool. Observe any changes to your design. ❹ Repeat the activity with another piece of PS, but this time, consider how much the item will shrink as you plan your design. Estimate how large the original design must be to make the shrunken item the size you want. Use a hole punch to make a hole if you plan to use the shrunken object on a chain or ribbon. (Remember, the hole will shrink.) Heat as previously instructed.

Part B: Polystyrene Shrink Test

Do polystyrene (PS) pieces shrink evenly in all directions?

Materials

✓clear, clean polystyrene (PS) containers (#6 recycle code) ✓scissors ✓ruler ✓centimeter graph paper ✓toaster oven or conventional oven (*not* a convection oven or microwave) ✓aluminum foil ✓oven mitt ✓(optional) commercial Shrinky Dinks® (available from K&B Innovations, Inc., North Lake, WI; 262/966-0305; *http://www.shrinkydinks.com*) or other PS for shrinking crafts such as Aleene's Shrink-It™, available from craft stores

Procedure

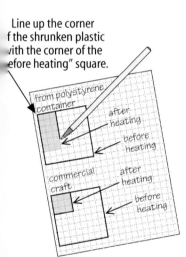

Line up the corner of the shrunken plastic with the corner of the "before heating" square.

❶ Cut out an 8-cm x 8-cm piece of polystyrene (PS). Calculate the area of the square piece (length x height). Trace your square on centimeter graph paper. Label this tracing "before heating." Count the number of boxes within the square. (Each box should be 1 cm x 1 cm.) This should equal the area you calculated previously. ❷ Shrink the PS square as instructed in Part A (steps 2 and 3). ❸ Measure and record the dimensions of the shrunken piece. What is its shape now? ❹ Line up one corner of the shrunken sample with the original square (as shown in the figure) and trace around it. Label the tracing "after heating." Calculate the area of the shrunken PS using the length x height formula and by counting the number of boxes covered. How do these areas compare? ❺ Subtract the shrunken area from the original area to determine the area lost during shrinkage. ❻ Calculate and record the percent shrinkage of the PS [(area lost ÷ original area) x 100 = percent shrinkage]. ❼ If you have commercial Shrinky Dinks, repeat the procedure and compare the results with those for the recyclable #6 PS.

Part C: Triangle Change

Materials

✓clear, clean polystyrene (PS) containers (#6 recycle code) ✓ (optional) Shrinky Dinks or other PS for shrinking crafts ✓scissors ✓ruler ✓centimeter graph paper ✓toaster oven or conventional oven (*not* a convection oven or microwave) ✓aluminum foil ✓oven mitt

Procedure

❶ Cut another 8-cm x 8-cm piece of polystyrene (PS). Draw a diagonal line between two opposite corners of the square to form two right triangles within the

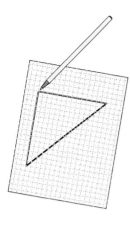

square. Cut along this diagonal line. ❷ Trace one of the right triangles on your graph paper. (See figure.) Determine the area of this triangle both by counting the number of squares within the triangle and using the following formula: area of a triangle = ½ (height x base). ❸ From your observations in Part B, predict what will happen to the shape and area of the triangle when heated in the oven. Try it!

References

Sarquis, J.L.; Sarquis, A.M.; Williams, J.P. "Shape Shifters," *Teaching Chemistry with TOYS—Activities for Grades K–9;* McGraw-Hill: New York, 1995.

Shrunken Treasures, Terrific Science at Home Kit; Terrific Science: Middletown, OH, 2001.

Polymers at Lunch

Fast-food salads, sandwiches, and drinks typically use packaging made from several different types of polymers. Next time you pick up lunch, check the recycling symbols on your food containers. You may find foamed polystyrene, low-density polyethylene, or other polymers. After lunch, look for the nearest recycling bin!

Invisible Crystals

Now you see 'em; now you don't….The invisible crystals in this lesson are actually the polymer *sodium polyacrylamide,* sold as Soil Moist™ for use in gardening. This polymer can absorb many hundred times its own weight in water. The hydrated crystals are mostly water, which gives them some very interesting properties—including invisibility in water.

Why can you see water in a glass but not these hydrated crystals in water? The answer has to do with the way light travels through different substances. Light refracts (or bends) differently when it travels through glass than when it travels through water. We say that these two materials have different indexes of refraction. This phenomenon makes both the glass and the water visible. This same phenomenon also causes the hydrated crystals to seem invisible when they're placed in water. Why? Because the hydrated sodium polyacrylamide crystals are mostly water, so light travels through them about the same as it would through plain water. The crystals reappear when they're lifted out into the air because the indexes of refraction are very different for air and the crystals. This also accounts for why you can see air bubbles that may be trapped in the hydrated crystals.

Safety for All Parts

Avoid ingestion, inhalation, or eye contact with the sodium polyacrylamide. Should contact with the eyes occur, rinse with water and seek medical attention.

Part A: Crystal on a String

Materials

✔ beaker ✔ sodium polyacrylamide crystals (available from scientific supply houses or as Soil Moist from most garden stores; see *http://www.soilmoist.com* for online sources) ✔ thread or thin string ✔ food color ✔ water (deionized or distilled water works best, but tap water will also work)

Procedure

❶ Put a few inches of water into a beaker. ❷ Drop five or six polyacrylamide crystals into the water and set aside for several hours. ❸ Observe the crystals several times during this growing period. How is the appearance of the crystals changing? When the crystals are fully grown, they will be invisible in water. If bubbles form in the crystals, place the jar in a refrigerator for several hours. Then allow it to warm back to room temperature. The dissolved gas will exit at the water's surface. ❹ Remove one of the hydrated crystals and wrap a thread or string around it

0   1   2

centimeters

two or three times to form a "noose" or "cage" to hold it securely; then tie the string. (See figure.) This may take some practice; the crystals are rubbery and may split in half if tied too tightly. Bigger crystals are easier to tie a string to. ❺ Use the string to suspend the hydrated crystal in the water. What do you see? Lift the crystal in and out of the water. What changes do you see? ❻ Try dipping the crystal in colored water.

Part B: Overhead Projector Demonstration

Materials

✓ beaker ✓ sodium polyacrylamide crystals ✓ overhead projector ✓ overhead transparency ✓ overhead marker ✓ water

Procedure

❶ Hydrate enough crystals to cover the bottom of the beaker. ❷ On an overhead transparency, write a message that the beaker will cover. Place the transparency on the projector screen and place the beaker over the message. ❸ Turn on the overhead projector—the message will be invisible. ❹ Add water to the beaker and *voilà*—the message appears!

References

Just Add Water for Great Science, Terrific Science Kit; Terrific Science: Middletown, OH, 1998.

Totally Awesome Family Science Stuff, Terrific Science Kit; Terrific Science: Middletown, OH, 1998.

Be Cool

Sodium polyacrylamide crystals don't just help your plants grow, they can also keep you cool in the summer. Runners, bicyclists, and others who spend considerable time outdoors often use cloth collars with these crystals sewn inside. The collar is soaked in water for several hours, then worn around the neck. The evaporation of the water from the collar helps cool the body the same way perspiration does. The advantage of using a cool collar over a plain wet cloth is that the crystals release their water very slowly, affording longer periods of cooling before the collar has to be wetted again.

Super Slurper

How can disposable baby diapers absorb so much liquid? They contain a superabsorbent polymer called *sodium polyacrylate*—also known as "super slurper." Besides being the key ingredient in high absorbency diapers, it is also used (along with related polymers) in alkaline batteries, feminine hygiene products, water beds, and as a fuel filtration material to remove moisture from automobile and jet fuels.

Superabsorbent materials were first developed for use in agriculture (as thickeners and for water retention) and in the oil industry (as additives in drilling fluid in offshore operations). Some superabsorbent materials absorb as much as 2,000 times their own weight in water. In the process of absorbing so much water, the powdered polymer turns into a gel. In general, when table salt or other water-soluble ionic compounds are added to the gel, the gel releases the water and liquefies. However, the addition of non-ionic compounds like sugar does not appear to affect the gel. Because tap water contains dissolved ionic compounds, the polymer does not gel as well in tap water as it does in distilled water. The sodium polyacrylate used in this lesson, for example, can absorb about 800 times its weight in distilled water, but only 300 times its weight in tap water. It should not surprise you to learn that only about 50 times its weight in water can be absorbed if the polymer is placed in a 1% saltwater solution.

Safety for All Parts

Avoid ingestion, inhalation, or eye contact with the sodium polyacrylate. Should contact with the eyes occur, rinse with water and seek medical attention.

Disposal for All Parts

Dispose of excess powder and/or gelled material in the trash, not down the drain.

Part A: Experimenting with Super Slurper

Materials

✓clear plastic cups ✓measuring spoons ✓water ✓sodium polyacrylate (available from Flinn Scientific, Batavia, IL; 800/452-1261; *http://www.flinnsci.com*) ✓sodium chloride (table salt) ✓sugar ✓baking soda ✓salt substitute

Procedure

❶ Pour ¼ teaspoon sodium polyacrylate into a cup. ❷ Pour 1 tablespoon water into the cup. Observe and describe what you see. ❸ Determine how much more water the polymer can hold, by adding water 1 tablespoon at a time and recording and keeping track of how much is added. Wait about 10–15 seconds between additions. Stop when no more water is absorbed. ❹ Divide the gelled super slurper into four or five cups, putting roughly equal amounts in each. ❺ Sprinkle a little table salt over the super slurper in one of the cups and stir. Sprinkle more salt until the gel becomes liquid. ❻ Repeat step 5 using sugar, baking soda, salt substitute, and/or similar substances. Which substance took the least amount to de-gel the polymer? Which had the least effect on the gelled polymer?

Part B: How Much Water Can a Disposable Diaper Hold?

Materials

✓disposable diapers containing superabsorbent materials ✓measuring spoons and cups ✓container ✓water ✓sodium chloride (table salt)

Procedure

❶ Design an experiment to determine how much water a disposable diaper will hold. ❷ Repeat the experiment using saltwater and compare the results.

References

Katz, D.A. "Instant Glop," *Investigations in Chemistry.* 1988.

Flinn Scientific. "Superabsorbent Polymers," *CHEM FAX.* 1990.

Fire-Fighting Diapers

An uncharred diaper found after a trash fire gave a Florida fire fighter the idea for a new tool to battle fires. Superabsorbent polyacrylamide, similar to the polymer in disposable diapers, now has a new use in preventing loss of life and property from brush or forest fires. Once saturated with water, this superabsorbent material forms a gel-like substance that can be sprayed on houses or other structures. After the building is covered, the gel acts like a wall of sticky water that can hold back flames as hot as 2,000°F. This superabsorbent polymer can hold a fire at bay for an hour or more, leaving adequate time to rescue trapped people or livestock. It also allows fire fighters more time to battle the blaze and perhaps save the building.

Polymers and Polarized Light

Have you ever laid two pairs of Polaroid® sunglasses on top of each other? If you rotate the lenses of one pair relative to the other, you will observe that the amount of light coming through these two layers changes quite dramatically.

Usually, the lightwaves around us travel in all directions. However, if a polarizer is placed in the path of light, only the light in a single plane can pass through. This effect is shown below by polarizer (a). The plane of light can continue through the second layer of polarizing material (b) if the two layers are parallel to one another. But the light will be stopped if the layers are perpendicular (at a 90° angle) to one another. As the layers rotate from a parallel to a perpendicular orientation, less and less light is able to pass through.

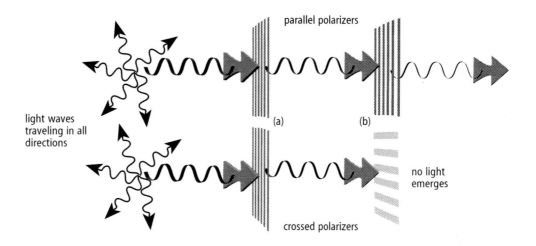

You may be surprised by what happens if you place a piece of cellophane tape or a cellophane candy wrapper between the two crossed polarizers. Although no light came through the crossed polarizers before, light comes through now. Why? Cellophane tape and other optically active materials have the ability to rotate the plane of light that passes through them. Thus, if an optically active material is placed between two crossed polarizers, some light will pass through. This effect is shown below.

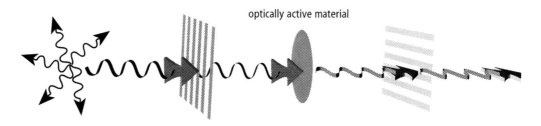

Many thin polymer films are optically active. They have this property because they are stretched when manufactured and their molecules orient in the direction of the stretch. When light shines through these polymer films, the orientation of the polymer molecules affects the movement of light.

Part A: Overhead Projector Demonstration

Materials

✓2 polarizing filters (6 inch x 6 inch, available from Educational Innovations, Norwalk, CT; 888/912-7474; *http://www.teachersource.com)* ✓overhead projector ✓transparent, molded polystyrene (PS) objects (for example, petri dish, utensils, cup, deli container, protractor, ruler) ✓cellophane (for example, candy wrappers) ✓inexpensive cellophane tape

Procedure

❶ Lay one of the polarizing filters on the stage of the overhead projector and tape the second filter over the glass on the head of the overhead projector. ❷ Rotate the polarizing filter on the stage to show the variations in the amount of light that will pass through at different orientations. Determine the position where the two filters are perpendicular (at a 90° angle, when no light passes through). ❸ Place the various polystyrene (PS) objects on top of the filter on the stage and observe. Try rotating the polarizing filter on the stage while holding the objects still and observe. ❹ Flatten a piece of cellophane wrapper and place it on the stage. Observe the color changes as you fold the cellophane in many directions and rotate the folded wrapper. Are the color changes random or do they follow a definite pattern? ❺ Put pieces of cellophane tape on the polarizing filter. Experiment with a variety of directions and layers.

Part B: Cellophane Tape Kaleidoscope

Inexpensive cellophane tape may not be ideal for sticking things together, but it is an optically active polymer that you can use to make a wonderful homemade kaleidoscope. The different layers and orientations of cellophane tape on the kaleidoscope rotate the polarized light in different ways, producing many colors. With every 90° rotation, the visible light switches from one color to its complementary color.

Materials

✓2 polarizing filters (3 inch x 3 inch) ✓cardboard tube from bathroom tissue or paper towels ✓slightly larger diameter cardboard tube or 5-ounce paper cup ✓inexpensive cellophane tape (do not use Scotch® brand Magic™ tape) ✓felt-tipped pen or marker ✓scissors

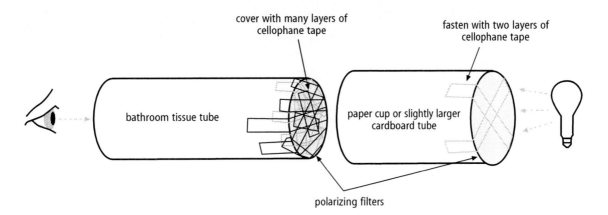

cover with many layers of
cellophane tape

fasten with two layers of
cellophane tape

bathroom tissue tube

paper cup or slightly larger
cardboard tube

polarizing filters

Procedure

❶ Place one end of the smaller cardboard tube on a polarizing filter and trace around the tube with a felt-tipped pen or marker. Cut out the circle. ❷ Tape the circle to the end of the tube with cellophane tape, randomly placing many different-sized pieces of the tape. The more layers the better! (See figure.)
❸ If using the paper cup, cut out the bottom. Repeat step 1 with the paper cup or second cardboard tube. Tape on the second circle using only two pieces of tape.
❹ Place the cup or tube from step 3 over the end of the smaller tube. ❺ Point the kaleidoscope at a light source and look through it; rotate the paper cup or larger tube and observe!

References

Sherman, M.C. "Cellophane Tape Kaleidoscope," *Fun with Polymers;* 1991.

"Cellophane Tape Kaleidoscope," *Chain Gang—The Chemistry of Polymers;* Sarquis, A.M., Ed.; Science in Our World Series; Terrific Science: Middletown, OH, 1999.

National Science Education Standards Matrix

This matrix shows how the activities in this book relate to the National Science Education Standards. The standards are taken from *National Science Education Standards*; National Research Council; National Academy: Washington, D.C., 1996.

Activities	Science as Inquiry — Abilities Necessary to Do Scientific Inquiry				Physical Science — Properties of Objects and Materials		Physical Science — Light, Heat, Electricity, and Magnetism
NSES Grade Level	Design and conduct a scientific investigation. (K–12)	Use appropriate tools and techniques to gather, analyze, and interpret data. (K–12)	Develop descriptions, explanations, predictions, and models using evidence. (K–12)	Think critically and logically to understand the relationships between evidence and explanations. (K–12)	Objects have many observable properties, including size, weight, shape, color, temperature, and the ability to react with other substances. Those properties can be measured using tools, such as rulers, balances, and thermometers. (K–4)	Objects are made of one or more materials, such as paper, wood, and metal. Objects can be described by the properties of the materials from which they are made, and those properties can be used to separate or sort a group of objects or materials. (K–4)	Light travels in a straight line until it strikes an object. Light can be reflected by a mirror, refracted by a lens, or absorbed by the object. (K–4)
Polymers and Polarized Light	◆		◆	◆	◆		◆
Super Slurper		◆					
Invisible Crystals	◆				◆		
The Amazing Shrinking Plastic	◆		◆				
Skewering Polymers	◆		◆		◆		
Polymer Stretch Test	◆	◆			◆		
Defoaming Packing Peanuts	◆						
Polyvinyl Alcohol	◆	◆	◆				
Gluep	◆	◆			◆		
Testing Polymer Densities	◆	◆	◆		◆	◆	

Physical Science

Properties and Changes of Properties in Matter

A substance has characteristic properties, such as density, a boiling point, and solubility, all of which are independent of the amount of the sample. A mixture of substances often can be separated into the original substances using one or more of these characteristic properties. — 5–8

Substances react chemically in characteristic ways with other substances (compounds) with different characteristic properties. In chemical reactions, the total mass is conserved. Substances often are placed in categories or groups if they react in similar ways; an example of such a group is metals. — 5–8

Transfer of Energy

Light interacts with matter by transmission (including refraction), absorption, or scattering (including reflection). To see an object, light from that object—emitted by or scattered from it—must enter the eye. — 5–8

Structure and Properties of Matter

The physical properties of compounds reflect the nature of the interactions among its molecules. — 9–12

Chemical Reactions

Chemical reactions occur all around us, for example in health care, cooking, cosmetics, and automobiles. — 9–12

History and Nature of Science

Science as a Human Endeavor

Scientists are influenced by societal, cultural, and personal beliefs and ways of viewing the world. — 9–12

Science and Technology

Understandings about Science and Technology

Science often advances with introduction of new technologies. — 9–12

Abilities of Technological Design

Identify a problem or design an opportunity. — 9–12

Evaluate the solution and its consequences. — 9–12